A PARENT'S GUIDE

DYSLEXIA

AND OTHER LEARNING DIFFICULTIES

DYSPRAXIA

GIFTED CHILDREN

ATTENTION DEFICIT DISORDER

DIAGNOSIS

VISION TRAINING

HYPERACTIVITY

Need2Know

MARIA CHIVERS

First published by Need2Know 1997
Need2Know, Remus House, Coltsfoot Drive, Woodston,
Peterborough PE2 9JX

Edited by Kerrie Pateman
Typesetting by Forward Press Ltd

A PARENT'S GUIDE TO DYSLEXIA AND OTHER LEARNING DIFFICULTIES

Contents

Contributors

Dr D Cowell B.Sc. M.Phil. Ph.D. Dip. Psych.
David Cowell took Psychology with Physiology at
Manchester University, before training as an educational
psychologist at the Tavistock Centre in London. He has an
M.Phil and PhD from Exeter University. He has worked as
an educational psychologist in Durham, Huddersfield and
Swindon, and was Head of the Area's Services in the
latter. David has produced many varied publications.

David worked in Leicestershire, in a varied role which
included a project on *school phobia*, and liaising between
the School Psychological Service and hospital-based Child
Psychiatry. He left in December 1996 to undertake a
variety of activities in schools, universities and publishing.

Keith Holland B.Sc, FBCO,DCLP
Keith is an optometrist practising in Cheltenham,
Gloucestershire, with a special interest in vision and
learning. Over the last ten years he has built up one of the
largest specialist practices in Europe, dealing with the
visual problems associated with dyslexia and learning
difficulties. Keith has published many articles on the links
between vision and literacy and lectures widely on the
subject, both at home and abroad. He is founder and
chairman of the British Association of Behavioural
Optometrists, a professional special interest group that
represents practioners around Britain working in this field.
He is married and has four children.

Christine Robinson DBO, SRO

Born and educated in Birmingham, England. Christine trained as an orthoptist at the Children's Hospital, Birmingham, and worked at Princess Margaret Hospital, Swindon since 1964. She is married with three sons, two of whom are dyslexic. Christine has had an interest in dyslexia for the last 20 years, and enjoys assessing and helping children who are dyslexic. She finds it useful to be able to see the problems from two different perspectives - a parent of dyslexic children and as a professional who is able to advise and treat.

Sylvia Jeffs

Sylvia Jeffs left grammar school at 16 to help with the family business. After marriage and fostering 17 children, she furthered her education and spent a short time as a primary teacher before entering the civil service. Her Inland Revenue career ended in 1978 when her son was born with Down's syndrome. She educated him at home, and for 12 years also worked voluntarily for the organisation *Education Otherwise* on their legal group and as their special needs adviser.

Dr Richard Eyres B.Sc, M.B., B.S., M.R.C., Psyc.

Dr Richard Eyres is a member of the Royal College of Psychiatrists and Consultant in Child and Adolescent Psychiatry at Princess Margaret Hospital in Swindon. Having completed higher training at The Maudsley and Kings College Hospitals he developed interests in Adolescent Psychiatry and Family Therapy. As Consultant

Psychiatrist in Richmond between 1991-94 he worked closely with the local authority Social Services Department and Education Department in developing inter-agency approaches to Child Protection issues and children with educational difficulties associated with school-based problems with behaviour and attendance. In Swindon he is now responsible particularly for Special Services for children under the age of eight years.

Author Acknowledgements
Please note that, for ease of reading, *he* should be transposed for *she* when appropriate. I have also talked about *mothers* rather than *fathers* because the vast majority of parents having the most dealings with young children are still their mothers.

I would like to express my thanks to all the staff at the Swindon Dyslexia Centre, and in particular Georgie James, the Manager, for all their help and assistance in preparing this book.

Thanks are also extended to:

The specialists who have contributed to this book: Dr D Cowell B.Sc. M.Phil. Ph.D. Dip. Psych., Christine Robinson DBO, SRO, Keith Holland B.Sc, FBCO,DCLP, Dr Richard Eyres B.Sc, M.B., B.S., M.R.C., Psyc., Sylvia Jeffs and the British Dyslexia Association - for all their help, and Network 81 - who have kindly allowed me to use some of their forms.

Dedication
This book is dedicated to the hundreds of thousands of parents, who battle every day with bureaucracy to get equal rights for their children in schools.

Introduction

I wrote this book to help parents through the minefield of SEN. I wanted to show them the quickest way to get their child's problems identified, and to describe some of the services and specialists available for early assessment.

I had first hand experience of the problems of identifying dyslexia, eight years ago, when both my sons were diagnosed as dyslexic by an educational psychologist. Prior to this I had been fighting the education system for some time, trying to tell the school that something was wrong, and endeavouring to get them extra help and tuition. Some people didn't believe that dyslexia existed, they thought it was some *middle-class disease*. However, I am glad to say, times are slowly changing and dyslexia is now a recognised learning difficulty.

Dyslexia affects 4% of the population - adults and children. Many people who are dyslexic or have Specific Learning Difficulties are extremely bright, yet fail to reach their full potential. Many people ask, 'What is dyslexia?' Dyslexia and Specific Learning Difficulties often come under the same umbrella. The word dyslexic comes from the Greek meaning *difficulty with words or language*. Throughout this book I will be explaining about a few of the different learning difficulties people are faced with.

This book shows you:

- The signs for early identification.
- Where to get help.
- How to get help.

- What other professional services are involved, ie psychologist, psychiatrist etc.

- What help you are legally entitled to.

- How to set up a support group.

Having dyslexia is not the end of the world. With support and tuition, it *can* be overcome.

I hope this book will be invaluable, to dyslexics, their parents, teachers and other professionals.

If this book leads to greater public awareness of dyslexia and makes it easier for people to get the help they need, then it will have achieved its purpose.

1 I KNOW THERE IS SOMETHING WRONG

DYSPRAXIA
GIFTED CHILDREN
ATTENTION DEFICIT DISORDER
DIAGNOSIS
VISION TRAINING
HYPERACTIVITY

- What should I do...
- Seeking help
- What is a Statement?
- Is there light at the end of the tunnel?
- Questions, questions, questions
- Summing up...

Every mother knows when there is something wrong with their child. But finding out *exactly* what is wrong can prove to be difficult. This was the problem I was faced with as both my sons were having serious problems at school and were subsequently diagnosed as dyslexic. At that time, hardly anyone knew what the term meant, and I was at a total loss to know what to do about it.

Along with many other parents, I found it extremely frustrating to be told that my child is: *just naughty, lazy, slow,* or *will not listen.* Many children are desperately unhappy as they go through their school life at the bottom of the class, knowing the answers but never being able to put them on paper.

Something had to be done, but I didn't know what. Every few weeks I went to see my son's teacher to explain how worried I was. But repeatedly and by several different teachers, I was told that *boys are slower than girls* and *he would catch up*. At the back of my mind, I knew that this was wrong!

What should I do?

What should I do? If I went to the school continually it might cause a lot of bad feeling. I didn't know what to do or who to turn to. Friends said go to the headmistress - but I had spoken to her many times during the past three years and it did not improve matters. Perhaps my child really was slow or backward! Perhaps he would never catch up!

A very good friend (and a teacher at this same school) said to me:

'What does it matter if he doesn't amount to anything? You will love him just as much no matter what he does. At the end of the day, education isn't everything.'

Of course I would love him no matter what he did. But that wasn't the point. I believe a mother's love is unconditional. A mother's duty is to protect and provide the best she can for that child. As long as he does his best then it is irrelevant if he fails - because he only fails in the eyes of others. But if a child is bright and fails to achieve his potential, then *you are failing him* if you don't do anything about it.

Was I an over-anxious mother who expected too much of

him? What parent wouldn't be anxious with a child who couldn't read at nearly eight years of age? But *no-one would listen*.

Then things came to a head. Walking home from school with Jeremy one day, I could see he was worried. We talked, and his fears came rushing out. He knew he *wasn't the same as the others*. Distraught with worry, I decided I finally had to do something about it.

What could I do?

I contacted the county's educational psychologist. After explaining the position, he agreed to go into the school to carry out some tests. I was too frightened to tell the headmistress. The psychologist confirmed my fears. My son was very bright - but performing below his ability. He was dyslexic. The educational psychologist said a plan of action was needed immediately to stop him falling further behind.

Later I was summoned to see the headmistress and accused of going behind her back. I explained that I had asked for their help for three years and was getting nowhere. She refused to listen, and stated that I had made a big mistake as my son would always be labelled as *backward*.

But the psychologist assured me I had done the right thing. While some schools were reluctant to call in specialists, it was best to get the problems sorted out before they got worse.

Later I realised that in my naivety I had offended the headmistress. There is a procedure which one should follow and that does not involve keeping the head in the dark!

Whilst waiting for the written report from the educational psychologist we moved area. My son had only been at his new school for a few weeks when the headmaster noticed there was a problem. He was prepared to do something about it. The relief was overwhelming.

When the report came, it clearly showed that our son had *Specific Learning Difficulties*. What on earth did that mean? How could I help? Who could help and where could I find them? What was the school obliged to do and were they going to do it?

Seeking help

My first point of call was to the library, who were very helpful. They suggested contacting the British Dyslexia Association as *Specific Learning Difficulties* often comes under this heading. The local Association explained about an assessment which identified areas of weakness as well as identifying strengths.

Incidently, up to that point my county's psychological service refused to put *dyslexic* on their reports. This has now been changed, although certain counties still *refuse to do so*.

Jeremy was offered a place locally with the Dyslexia Association and started attending weekly classes for an hour. The improvement was quite dramatic. His confidence started to increase as he saw other children with the same problems. He realised he was not alone.

What is a Statement?

Just as Jeremy started his weekly classes, the school contacted us about our other son, Mark. He was also falling behind at school. The school explained that they wanted to put a *Statement* on him. My immediate reaction was, *what on earth is a Statement?*

The statementing process simply means putting a *Statement of Education* in place. Formally identifying a problem, directing the school and other professional services into place to safeguard the child's future (see page 39 for full statementing procedures).

I worked very closely with the school and other professionals and Mark's *Statement of Educational Needs* came through very quickly. Some parents call our helpline and say that in some cases it takes years to happen. This is against government guidance and is usually because the formal procedures are not put into place. Some leave matters to go on far too long before they formally ask for tests to be carried out (this procedure should take only 26 weeks).

Is there light at the end of the tunnel?

During the last eight years, both my children have made tremendous progress and *are now above average in most areas of the national curriculum*. So if you feel down about your child, there *is* light at the end of the tunnel - don't give up!

The local Dyslexia Association was keen to get me involved with the dyslexia movement. After a lot of help and advice, I opened an organisation called the Swindon Dyslexia Centre, for people with Specific Learning Difficulties. We employ specialist teachers and open between 9.30 and 6.30 six days a week.

Last year, we also set up a 'helpline' which has helped scores of people in our area. The parents who telephone say they feel so isolated, that they don't know where to go or who to turn to. We can give independent advice on

Specific Learning Difficulties. Most of these parents are desperate and at their wits end to know what to do about their child. If there is not a helpline in your area, how about setting one up? Many parents have the same worries as you do - so you can all support each other.

Some schools told parents that their child would have to move to a *special* school if he received a *Statement of Education*. This conflicts with what the Department of Education says. In the vast majority of cases, children stay at the same school.

Having received hundreds of calls during the last five years, I realised that there is plenty of help and information available, but the problem is - finding it! The DFE (Department for Education) has many excellent free leaflets on Special Educational Needs. As this information is available free to all parents, why is it not available in the foyer of every school?

Questions, questions, questions...

- Where can I get help?
- What help is available?
- How do you start looking for the information you require?
- What is dyslexia, dyspraxia, what is Attention Deficit Disorder?
- What is a *Statement of Educational Needs*? Should my child have one?
- If he has a *Statement,* will he have to go to a special school?

- What is my child legally entitled to?
- What is the LEA (Local Education Authority)?

These are the sort of questions repeatedly asked. Although the government has an Education Advisory Service, parents do not know where it is. They produce many different booklets about Special Educational Needs but parents are left in awe of the vast array of different books. Indeed in many instances you have to be widely educated yourself to make head or tail of the information. You also need to know where to get this information from in the first place.

It was at this point that I realised it would be helpful if the information was available in one book.

Summing up...

If you think there is something wrong with your child, then there probably is. Don't be put off with excuses that *boys are slower than girls, they'll soon catch up*, or *the school does not have sufficient money to offer any extra help*. Be assertive and ask for reading and spelling tests to be carried out.

2 SQUARE PEGS IN ROUND HOLES?

DYSPRAXIA

GIFTED CHILDREN

ATTENTION DEFICIT DISORDER

DIAGNOSIS

VISION TRAINING

HYPERACTIVITY

- Dyslexia/Specific Learning Difficulties
- Clumsy or dyspraxic?
- Hyperactivity or Attention Deficit Disorder
- Gifted children
- Summing up...

Special Needs Education covers a wide range of problems. From simple hearing or visual difficulties, through the broad spectrum of handicaps both physical and physiological to some of the severest handicaps ie mental handicap. Highly gifted children also come under this category and many parents of these children feel that they are often denied the monies desperately needed for their education.

There are hundreds and thousands of children struggling to come to terms with their education. Square pegs in round holes - it is very difficult for them to fit into the *normal education field*.

A lot of people suffer with learning difficulties - some of which are never recognised properly. Many of the disruptive children in schools are naughty simply because they do not fit into the system of *sitting, watching and listening* that prevails in the majority of educational establishments. These children need more help than the average child and this brings the problem of extra cost. The average child is allocated x number of pounds for their education but the children who do not fit into this equation cost the government more.

Will the schools identify a problem?

The biggest problem seems to be identifying exactly what is a *Special Educational Need*. One school will identify the problems early and start to put in the necessary help. Others will use delaying tactics for years - knowing that eventually the problems will be dealt with by another school, when the child moves on. Some Local Education Authorities (LEAs) are very good at recognising a child has problems in the first year or two at school - others are not so good.

Some teachers still believe that if children are born into families where adults and other children enjoy reading, then children will *automatically learn* to read. It is their belief that the child slowly builds up the necessary connections between what we say and the marks on a piece of paper. However for one reason or another, some children cannot seem to pick up these skills automatically and need a great deal of extra help.

The following pages explain a few of the *hidden disabilities* that are difficult to see and therefore difficult to assess. The most notable one being Attention Deficit Disorder (ADD), which is often seen by teachers and other parents as *children who are just spoilt* because they are often so naughty.

Dyslexia/Specific Learning Difficulties

Dyslexia and Specific Learning Difficulties often come under the same umbrella, causing confusion - especially among parents.

Dyslexia/Specific Learning Difficulties affects 4% of the population. Problems can show themselves in reading, writing, number work, short term memory, hand control and visual processing. Timekeeping, sense of direction and interpersonal skills can also be affected.

These difficulties often result in great frustration, bearing in mind that dyslexics are often of high or above average intelligence.

Dyslexia affects more males than females. Many of these children are extremely bright in lots of ways, always talking and asking questions. Yet they do not seem to reach their full potential in the academic field. A very good definition of dyslexia is by Dr J E Cullis, 1992, who wrote:

'Dyslexia means having difficulty with words in reading, spelling and writing - in spite of having normal intelligence and ability'.

Following is a checklist on dyslexia. However, you must remember that when children start school, they may make several of the mistakes listed. It is only if these symptoms continue beyond the time that the average child has grown out of them, they *may* indicate dyslexia and advice should be sought.

Dyslexia checklist

Reading and spelling
When your child reads and spells, does he frequently:

- Confuse letters that look similar: d - b, u - n, m - n
- Confuse letters that sound the same: v, f, th
- Reverse words: was - saw, now - won
- Transpose words: left - felt
- Read a word correctly and then further down the page, read it wrong
- Change the words around: the cat sat on the mat (the mat sat on the cat)
- Confuse small words: of, for, from
- When reading have difficulty in keeping the correct place on a line and frequently lose his place
- Read correctly but does not understand what he is reading

Writing
Even after frequent instruction does he still:

- Not know whether to use his right or left hand
- Leave out capital letters or use them in the wrong places
- Forget to dot the i's, and cross t's
- Form letters and numbers badly
- Writing slopes on the page and uses margins
- Use punctuation and paragraphs in the wrong places

Clumsy or dyspraxic?

Is your child just clumsy or does he have dyspraxia? What's the difference?

Every day you hear teachers and parents' alike saying 'Oh, he's always falling over, he's clumsy!' Obviously when the child is very young this may be correct but when it is all too frequent then this may be a sign of dyspraxia. Unfortunately many teachers and other professionals miss the vital signs and dismiss them as *clumsy*. All children who fall over, drop things and generally take longer to do things are not necessarily suffering with dyspraxia.

The medical journal defines dyspraxia as:

'A serious impairment in the development of motor or movement coordination that can't be explained solely in terms of mental retardation or any other specific inherited or acquired neurological disorder.'

What a mouthful! I understand it to mean ' *if they persistently continue to fall over and are clumsy, well after the age their other friends stopped'*.

Often this problem is accompanied by difficulties in vision and movement, ie problems with catching a ball, climbing stairs, tying shoelaces or writing. Some children may be only affected slightly, others more seriously. Sometimes developmental milestones are delayed and there might be speech difficulties. Children tend to drop things, stumble, bump into things and have poor handwriting. This, not surprisingly, leads on to difficulties at school. There is no known treatment at the moment, although regular *occupational therapy* may help.

Talking with your child's teacher will help them to understand the problem and will make others in the school aware of the problem. You can ask for occupational therapy to be provided at school. Some children have both dyslexia and dyspraxia.

Hyperactivity or Attention Deficit Disorder

A child who:

- can't concentrate
- moves around constantly
- has poor school performance in contrast with his intelligence
- has disruptive behaviour

Attention Deficit Disorder (ADD) and Attention Deficit Hyperactivity Disorder (ADHD), are names used for the same problem.

At times all children may be overactive and inattentive but hyperactive children are disruptive *nearly all the time*. ADD is thought to affect between 3% and 5% of the school age population. Some evidence exists to show that some 90% of sufferers are boys. If this condition is untreated, it can blight their adult life.

Ritalin is being prescribed after lengthy investigations by behavioural psychiatrists with some good results.

Hyperactivity/Attention Deficit Disorder checklist

Infants
- extreme restlessness, crying, poor sleep patterns
- difficult to feed
- constant thirst
- frequent tantrums, head banging and rocks the cot

Children
- poor concentration and brief attention span
- increased activity - always on the go
- impulsive - doesn't stop to think
- fearless and takes undue risks
- poor coordination - when tying laces, handwriting, ball games
- weak short term memory
- inflexible personality - uncooperative, defiant and disobedient
- problems with making friends
- lacks self esteem
- sleep and appetite problems continue
- normal or high IQ but under performance at school

Not all infants and children with ADD have all the features of the condition and there are different degrees of severity.

Adults
- most of the features of ADD in childhood remain

- employment may be difficult because of relationship problems and poor memory

- anti social behaviour may become so extreme it may lead to trouble with the law and to excess alcohol consumption

- poor self esteem may be distressing

Gifted children

At the other end of the scale is the gifted child, often not identified and who does not receive the correct education. Although these children do not fit into the *Special Educational Needs Definition*, their educational needs in many cases are not being met.

Hidden talent

Too many gifted children are unrecognised, unaided and misunderstood. If these children are not given the appropriate help they may become frustrated, angry and then start getting into trouble and disrupting classes. The help available differs tremendously from area to area. Once again it is up to the parents of these children to demand the appropriate help for their child.

- *Q*　What do you do with a child who is four years old, extremely bright, reads fluently, has mastered basic arithmetic, can tell you what an isthmus is, and draw a parallelogram?

  A　Kent County Council says 'the child should join the reception class at primary school because they don't move pupils up　as they would suffer socially'

The parents of the child strongly disagree. They point out that if the child was handicapped he would be sent to a special school and given one-to-one tuition. But because he's bright he is entitled to no extra help at all.

The mother says her child needs teaching at the right level, 'he soaks things up like a sponge. It would be a tragedy if he started going backwards'. Kent County Council like most councils' say 'they don't have any schools geared to *gifted children*'.

Giftedness is also a Special Need

At last one council appears to be doing something about the problem. London's borough of Wandsworth, has recently, formally recognised that '*giftedness is also a special need*'. They have launched what it calls its 'curriculum masterclasses'. Edward Lister, the council leader, said it would only be a matter of time before they found their way into a Government White Paper.

It is only in recent times that there appears to be a growing evidence of a sympathetic attitude to the very able. Many local education authorities are now realising the need to provide for this group of children.

The Gifted Children's Information Centre

Doctor Peter Congden, an educational psychologist, realised some years ago the desperate need for these children to be identified. He set up the *Gifted Children's Information Centre.* The Centre provides a great deal of help and support to parents and professionals alike.

It may be some time before all these children are identified as *gifted* and their needs put into place, but at least a start has been made!

Summing up...

Special Educational Needs covers a wide range of disabilities. The biggest problem is *identifying* a need. Without this it is difficult to put in the necessary help to support the child.

Most children should be able to stay in mainstream schooling with some additional help.

3 THE EDUCATION ACT - HOW DO I GET HELP?

- Code of Practice
- A Statement of Educational Needs
- Special Educational Needs Tribunal
- Summing up...

The 1993 Education Act, which is published by The Department of Education, lays down a *Code of Practice*, for schools *etc* to follow for children who have *learning difficulties significantly greater than other pupils of the same age.*

The *Code of Practice* sets out a 5-stage model of Special Educational Needs provision. It is important that these stages are followed so that any extra tuition can be provided as soon as possible, so that the child does not fall further behind.

What do I do if my child needs help?

If you are concerned that your child is under-achieving at school you should talk to his teacher. Many parents try to express their concerns with teachers early in the morning. This can cause problems because mornings are usually very busy for the teacher who has 30+ children. All these children will need some help with coats, buttons, zips etc. After school is probably the best time but it can help if you give the teacher a little time to prepare.

The fairest way for all concerned would be to explain quickly after school that you are concerned and ask if you could make an appointment in a couple of days time. Not only can the teacher be prepared for it, but so can you. What are your worries? Why are you concerned? Write a list and take it with you:

- Worried about John's reading

- Worried about his spelling

- He doesn't seem to have many friends

Parents tell me they still feel extremely intimidated when they go to the school. I still feel the same way even though I have been talking to head teachers for years. Don't let them make you feel that way. You are a *grown-up* too!

The first appointment

When you see the teacher, explain your fears. Go through your list. If you are worried about your child then you probably have cause to be - *a mother does know best!* After you have discussed everything with the teacher, tell her you will monitor the situation and contact her in about four weeks to see if there is any development.

Make a diary entry for four weeks time. When the time is up, if there has been no significant improvement contact the teacher again and make another appointment.

The second appointment

Once again, make a list before you go. Work down your list together and explain how you feel. If the teacher says things are improving and would like more time, monitor the situation for another few weeks.

The third appointment

If there has been no significant improvement and you are still concerned ask for another appointment. Before you go to the next meeting, write a letter with the points of concern. Point out that you have waited over two months for things to improve and you are extremely concerned at your child's lack of progress and that you would like the matter looked into officially. Address this letter to the teacher concerned but give a copy to the head teacher. Don't be put off!

The letter could say something like this:

```
Dear  Miss  (name)

As  you  are  aware,  I  have  been  speaking  to
you  since  (look  in  the  diary)  concerning
Peter's  lack  of  progress.

I  am  particularly  concerned  that  he  is
still  not  able  to  read,  write  and  so
forth  and  as  we  have  been  trying  to  solve
the  problem  for  several  months,  I  would
like  to  officially  request  that  some
tests  are  carried  out  to  see  exactly  what
his  reading  and  spelling  ages  are.

Yours  sincerely

(Your  name)


c.c. The Head Teacher
```

It is vital to keep a list of the dates of *every* visit to the school and what the outcome of each meeting was. This is extremely important in officially identifying an *educational need*. These notes will be needed later on. Once you have given a letter to the teacher (and a copy to the Head teacher), you are effectively asking for the first stage of the *Assessment Procedures* to be put into place.

Code of Practice

Special Educational Needs (SENs)

The 1993 Act hoped to tackle the *all or nothing* situation by issuing the *Code of Practice.*

A child has 'Special Educational Needs' if he has a learning difficulty which calls for 'special educational provisions' to be made for him. A child has a 'learning difficulty' if he has a significantly greater difficulty in learning than the majority of children his age, or has a disability which either prevents or hinders him from making use of the educational facilities generally provided in schools (in his Local Education Authority). 'Special educational provision' means educational provision which is additional to or otherwise different from that made generally for children of his age in schools (in his LEA).

Key factors

Proper *identification, assessment and evaluation* are key factors in succeeding with children with Special Educational Needs. Most children do not have Statements and rely on their schools for help. Previously, help was often not available without a Statement so there was a constant battle for them.

Code of Practice - five stages of help

Stages	What kind of help?	Organised by
1	Class or a year tutor identifies a child's special educational need, gathers information, consults with SEN Coordinator, and takes early action. Parents *can* express concern at this stage.	School
2	SEN coordinator takes responsibility for coordinating special educational provision and ensures that an individual education plan is drawn up, with a child's teachers.	School
3	SEN coordinator brings in outside specialists. At each stage the extra help must be monitored and reviewed to ensure that it is effectively meeting individual needs. Parents should be consulted. School governors must ensure that any child entitled to special educational provision is provided it. All schools must have a policy on special educational needs. They must have means of evaluating the success of the education provided. If the school cannot meet the child's special educational needs from its own resources, they should ask the LEA to start a 'statutory' assessment. Parents can also ask the LEA to make a statutory assessment.	School
4	LEA considers need for statutory and assessment and, if appropriate, LEA makes a multidisciplinary assessment.	School and LEA
5	LEA considers need for a Statement of Educational Needs and if appropriate, makes LEA a Statement and arranges, monitors and reviews provision. A child needs a Statement if it is necessary for the LEA to decide the special educational provision a child needs.	School and LEA

Code of Practice (school-based stages)

Parents are strongly advised to seek independent help from the various voluntary organisations at the early stages of *Statementing* because understanding the process can prevent a lot of problems later on. New regulations impose time limits for completing assessments and the whole process should take no longer than six months.

What does a Statement mean?

A lot of parents are confused by the term *Statement*. This comes from the 1981 Education Act. It states that a *Statutory Statement of Special Educational Needs* must be carried out where there is concern for a child's educational ability (after assessment). A full assessment of your child will be carried out. This means that the Chief Education Officer will ask for reports and advice from the following people:

- *Head Teacher* - The head will have asked for reports from everyone who has dealings with your child

- *Education Authority* - The Authority's own Psychologist will advise the Education Authority about your child's abilities, and the stages of development he has reached. He will then suggest ways of helping your child in the future

- *Medical* - A doctor will give your child a medical examination to see if there are any medical reasons for the problems at school

- *Social Services* - If Social Services have been involved with your family recently, they will be asked for a report

Following is an assessment contacts sheet.

Assessment form

Organisation	Name of contact	Tel no.
Special Needs Liaison Education Officer		
Contact person in Education Authority/ Named Officer		
Contact person at school Special Needs Coordinator		
Pre School		
Portage		
Nursery School		
Educational Psychologist		
Clinical Medical Officer		
Speech Therapist		
Occupational Therapist		
Social Worker		
Others		

Your views are important

Your views are very important. If you have queries then ask for a meeting to sort them out before you sign the Statement. You may, for instance, feel your child *should not have to cope* with learning a foreign language. He *can be excused* from this part of the National Curriculum *if it is written into his Statement*.

If your child uses a wordprocessor, it is also a good idea to try to get them to write into the Statement that, *the child should use a wordprocessor*. This is extremely useful later on for exams etc (see page 100).

Some questions you may like to think about are:

- How do you think your child compares with others of the same age?

- What are your worries and concerns about your child?

- What do you think your child's educational needs are?

- How do you think these can best be provided?

- How do you think your child sees his difficulties?

- Is there any information you would like to give me from other schools, doctors etc?

A Statement of Educational Needs

A Statement of Educational Needs is set out in six parts:

- **Part 1**
  Lists your own and your child's personal details

- **Part 2**

  Details the learning difficulties and disabilities your child has

- **Part 3**

  Lists the help that the LEA says your child should have in relation to:

  meeting the needs set out in part 2

  the long term objectives to be achieved by that special help

  the short-term targets

  regularly reviewing your child's progress towards those targets

- **Part 4**

  Informs you of the school your child will attend to get the help as set out in part 3, or the arrangements for education if it is to be outside school

- **Part 5**

  Describes any non-educational needs your child has ie transport to school

- **Part 6**

  Describes how your child will get the help described in part 5

Please refer to the Statement of Educational Needs table opposite.

Special Educational Needs Tribunal

What if I am not happy with the Local Education Authority's decision?

The Special Education Needs Tribunal, is an Independent Tribunal, which was set up by the Education Act 1993 to help parents, who disagreed with their Local Education Authority's decision.

Statement of Educational Needs

Dates of stages in my child's assessments	Date
1 Received first letter saying Education Authority wish to assess my child Replied on	
2 Education Psychologist assesses child	
3 Second letter from Education Authority saying they intend to go ahead with the assessment Sent in parental views Other Assessments: Medical Speech therapist Other reports	
4 Letter from Education Authority saying the assessment has been completed and a proposed Statement will be issued	
5 Proposed Statement arrives: make appointment with officer named in letter if wish to discuss it Confirm appointment in writing and reason for not accepting statement Confirm acceptance of proposed Statement New proposed Statement issued if necessary	
6 Final Statement issued; write acceptance *or* write requesting an Appeal	
7 Review date: Your child's Statement must be reviewed within one year of the date of the final statement - make a note in your diary	

You may appeal to the Tribunal against your LEA, if they:

- refuse to make a formal assessment following a parent's request

- refuse to issue a statement after a formal assessment

- have not named the school

- refuse to change the name of school

- cease to maintain a Statement

Time limits

Appeals must be sent to the Tribunal within two months of the LEA's decision, stating what you are appealing against.

Still unhappy?

If you are unhappy about these issues, you should contact the school and/or the LEA first. If you are still not satisfied, you may contact the Secretary of State stating that the school/LEA is acting unreasonably - or failing to carry out their duties.

Three very useful booklets, which are free and available from the Department for Education are:

- Special Education Needs, A Guide for Parents

- The Codes of Practice

- A Tribunal Guide

There are many voluntary organisations which can also help. *Advisory Centre for Education (ACE)* publish a useful handbook on Special Educational Needs, at £8. *Network 81* publish several good books/leaflets and advise on the Statementing procedures and appeals. The British Dyslexia Association have various books that can help. All addresses in the Help List at the back of the book.

Summing up...

If your child needs *more help than the average child of the same age*, these needs *must* be met.

Speak to your child's teacher as soon as you realise there is a problem. Don't get put off over and over again. Obviously allow the teacher time, but if there is no real progress you must begin *formal* procedures as soon as you can - ensuring the child's needs are identified and any help is put in place as soon as possible.

Don't worry about the assessment procedures - there are lots of people who can help you through this difficult time.

4 THE ROLE OF THE PSYCHOLOGIST AND PSYCHIATRIST

- Five stages
- The educational psychologist's report
- Headings for reports
- Where can I find an educational psychologist?
- The role of Child Mental-Health services in Specific Learning Difficulties
- Summing up...

By Dr. David Cowell B.SC. M.Phil. Ph.D. Dip. Psych.

This section describes the role of the educational psychologist, with particular reference to the 1996 Education Act. This Act has a consolidating function; namely, it pulls together the whole of the 1944 and 1993 Acts. However, the *Code of Practice*, which was published alongside the 1993 Act, remains operative.

The 1944 Act defined the guidelines for special educational provision for many years. This specified a range of largely medically-related difficulties, including blindness, partial sight, hearing impairment, epilepsy, low intellectual ability, and *delicacy*. As most people working in the special education field know, the 1981 Education Act which was based upon the Warnock Report of 1979, required Education Authorities to consider children's Special Educational Needs on a broader basis than had been the case. The new legislation referred only to *learning difficulties significantly greater than other pupils of the same age*. The 1993 Act extended and clarified the 1981 Act, giving, among other things, an entitlement for parents to appeal to an impartial, governmentally-supported Tribunal. The 1993 Act also required Local Education Authorities to complete their assessments within 26 weeks of stating statutory assessment is to be undertaken.

For many years, about 2% of children had received long-term special educational help, and the Warnock report envisaged that this proportion would continue. This was a little surprising, in view of the more inclusive definition of special needs which had been adopted. In particular, one group of children - those with Specific Learning Difficulties - who did not come within the terms of the 1944 Act were able to be referred under the subsequent legislation. It was clear at the time that a higher proportion of children would therefore receive Statements of Special Need - an increase that Local Education Authorities did not seem to expect.

In retrospect, the 1981 and 1993 Acts particularly addressed what came to be known as the *Warnock 18%*. This was the large minority of pupils who would be likely to have Special Educational Needs for some time in their school careers.

This distinction between the large minority with temporary difficulties, and the small minority with greater problems, was instrumental in defining the *staged assessment of the 1993 Act*. According to the terms of this step-by-step approach, children would move through a series of stages which would progressively diagnose their problems and ways in which they might be helped. This way of working presupposes the need for a filter process, which identifies the 2% or so who will become the subject of a Statement of Special Need, and also provides a stepwise helping procedure for that much larger number of pupils who require special educational help, for a few weeks, months, or years, in their own schools. However, for a small number of needy children, a full multi-disciplinary assessment of Special Educational Needs can be carried out at once.

The Code of Practice applies to all Special Educational Needs, including emotional and behaviour difficulties.

Teachers and parents in private education should note that the Code of Practice recognises that some children in this sector do have Special Educational Needs - perhaps a larger proportion than is generally recognised. Indeed, the Code places a responsibility on LEAs to identify such children.

Five stages

Stage 1
This stage places the onus of responsibility on the class teacher (mainly in primary schools, or subject teacher,

mainly in secondary schools). The class teacher tries to gather information about the pupil's performance in the classroom and tries to adapt as far as possible, the teaching content and methods to the pupil's individual needs. Stage one also requires the effectiveness of the helping procedures to be evaluated over time through a process of review.

Stage 2

Involves the seeking of further advice, normally from the school's Special Educational Needs Co-ordinator (SENCO) or others from within the school. At this stage, there should be a process of informal consultation with allied professionals, such as educational psychologists. Parents progressively involved at this stage.

Stage 3

The educational psychologist is fully involved at this stage. The SENCO continues to take a leading role, but the emphasis is upon the contribution which can be made by the external specialist, since by the end of Stage 2, the school have probably felt they had done as much as they reasonably can. At this stage, a new Individual Education Plan (IEP) is drawn up, which includes an input from advisory and specialist service. Monitoring and review arrangements are carefully specified. Educational psychologists frequently describe their reports at this stage as being to *inform* Stage 3. This does not necessarily represent a full assessment by the educational psychologist. After at least two reviews at Stage 3, the Head Teacher of the school (not the educational psychologist) may consider referring the child to the LEA for a Statutory Assessment.

Children may, however, be brought to the LEA's attention for Stage 4 by a number of groups, including the school referral as noted above. Parents may request assessment, in which case the LEA will normally seek information from the school before agreeing. Other agencies, such as Medical Authorities, Child Guidance, or Social Services, may also make such requests.

Stage 4

It is this stage that the educational psychologist is required to write a full report, or appendix for the purpose of advising the LEA. One should note that independent practitioners, if they are fully qualified, may also contribute to the Statutory Assessment of the child and the LEA is bound by the Code to take account of their recommendations.

Stage 5

Stage five is for the LEA to consider the need for a statement of special needs and, if appropriate, makes a statement and arranges provision, together with a plan for monitoring and review.

The educational psychologist's report

What does, or should comprise the content of the educational psychologist's report is a matter of some contention both within and outside the profession. In general, LEAs lay down a guideline for their educational psychologists, and there is also a corpus of professional opinion which guides professional action. One difficulty is that educational psychologists' reports normally address a variety of audiences; the LEA, teachers, parents, other educational psychologists, allied professionals, such as medical personnel, and of course, the pupil in question.

A practical difficulty is that the amount of educational psychologist's time available to schools is strictly limited. In general, a small primary school will be 'allocated' approximately five working days per year. This is mainly for statutory work. Secondary schools will also have a time-allocation, which is calculated according to how the LEA views the needs of the particular school. At secondary school level, the educational psychologist will normally be the LEA representative for the important *Transition Review* - that is, the first which is carried out for a Statemented pupil after the pupil's fourteenth birthday. The Review, which includes a meeting with parents, enables the school to draw up a Transition Plan to guide the pupil's last years at school. Some secondary schools make substantial demands on the educational psychologist to assess pupils for Special Concessionary Arrangements at GCSE.

In general, educational psychologists will be careful to specify the reason for a referral, and will describe the background leading to it. Family difficulties are not directly relevant to Special Educational Needs, but may contribute to the building-up of a picture of the child and how he is developing. The contribution of other agencies will be noted. The educational psychologist will also be concerned to report on the kind of help the child has received, and how effective it has been.

The psychologist is particularly concerned with the general functioning of a pupil. An evaluation will need to be made of gross and fine motor skills, and the child's developing healthy independence. The assessment of scholastic attainment, particularly in literacy and numeracy will form an important section, normally with the use of nationally-standardised tests. Language difficulties will be described. The pupil's cognitive ability will also be evaluated, with a view to obtaining not only an overall measure, but also identifying areas of particular strength or weakness. Some difficulties, can be diagnosed through the identification of a particular *profile* of sub-test scores. The so-called *ACID* profile describes the relatively lower scores (four out of eleven on the full test) which are associated with such difficulties.

An interesting area of assessment is the pupil's approach to learning, and general behaviour in the classroom. It would be important to describe the particular aptitudes and interests shown by the pupil.

Will the psychologist listen to my views?
Psychologists are normally required to meet parents and discuss their views as part of the assessment process.

Parents are entitled to make their own representation to the LEA, but the educational psychologist will be careful to ensure that parental views are taken fully into account.

Can my child explain his difficulties?

Increasingly, pupils are helped to contribute to their own assessment. Secondary pupils can present written comments. Younger children might be helped to put their views forward through the use of a structured questionnaire. Young children's views have often been represented indirectly through their drawings, or the production of some other material.

Will my child have to follow the National Curriculum?

The educational psychologist must try to match the individual pupil to the national curriculum. Areas of particular weakness should be specified, and recommendations made as to how the child can best make progress.

Special equipment, facilities, and resources can be described, and the LEA may wish to provide these, perhaps on a loan basis.

How will I get my child to a school miles away?

General factors such as organisational and travel arrangements will be taken into account.

What is a short-term and long-term target?
Educational psychologists like to set immediate targets for helping. Longer-term aims can also help to guide the teaching and helping process.

A list of headings and subheadings follows, outlining the areas of enquiry which can be covered by educational psychologists.

Headings for reports

- Name of Pupil:
- Date of Birth:
- School:
- Telephone number of School:
- Contact at School:
- Name, address, and telephone number of parent:
- Date of Referral:

Reason for referral
- general learning difficulties
- Specific Learning Difficulties
- behaviour problems
- emotional difficulties
- sensory difficulties
- other (specify)

Background to referral
- history of difficulties going back to preschool
- difficulties for last few years
- difficulties evident since change of school
- difficulties only recently
- this is a re-referral

Relevant family factors
- similar difficulties at home and school
- pupil behaves well at home
- family disagreements, or relationship difficulties, contribute to pupil's problem

Other agencies involved
- Social services
- Child and family guidance
- Education welfare service
- Other (specify)

Current level and type of support/educational provision
- Support from a class teacher
- Help also from support assistant, SENCO, etc
- Other (specify)

Result of helping procedures

- Improvement in all areas of difficulty
- Improvement in some area (specify)
- Difficulties are worse
- New difficulties have become apparent (specify)

Pupil's current functioning

- Gross physical skills
- Fine motor skills
- Independence skills
- Scholastic attainment (use age/equivalent or standard scores)
- Receptive/expressive language normal for age
- Cognitive ability
- Approaches to learning/behaviour in the classroom situation
- Social behaviour with other children and adults
- Emotional factors responsive
- Particular aptitudes/interests shown by pupil (specify)
- Information reported by parents/others (specify)
- View of parents
- View of pupil

Type of curriculum needed

- Normal school curriculum
- Some degree of differentiation etc

Areas of the curriculum or areas of function where special programs of help are needed

- In literacy
- Maths etc
- Teaching methods and approaches recommended
- Equipment, facilities and resources required
- Educational, organisation and travel arrangements
- Immediate targets for education/helping
- Short-term aims
- Longer-term aims

Where can I find an educational psychologist?

The Association of educational psychologists will be pleased to send you a list of all educational psychologists practising in your area. See Help List for details.

Dr David Cowell

The Role of Child Mental-Health Services
By Dr Richard Eyres B.sc, M.B., B.S., M.R.C. Psyc.

Every district has its own Child and Adolescent Mental-Health Services. These may be found within a hospital setting or in a community-based clinic. They also may carry different service titles, eg Child Guidance, Child and Family Consultation, Child Psychiatry. In the past such clinics were often run in partnership with Education and Social Services, but nowadays they tend to be NHS resources. Referrals are accepted from all professionals working with children, and often from parents themselves.

Only in a minority of cases do children have mental illnesses seen in the adult population. The majority of children will have emotional or behavioural difficulties which they and their family can see are causing them problems in their normal social or educational progress. There will often be stressful factors in the background contributing to the presenting problem. These could include family break-up or relationship problems, bereavements, chronic physical illness, or school difficulties. The Child Mental-Health Services have a range of professionals who may be able to offer help, including psychiatrists, clinical psychologists, family therapists, community nurses, psychotherapists and specialist teachers. All these people will have regular links with schools and nurseries and the local authority.

Specific Learning Difficulties
Dyslexia is certainly one problem which may cause stress and distress in a child, leading to possible emotional and behaviour difficulties if not detected and appropriately managed in school. Most child psychiatrists prefer to use the term *Specific Learning Difficulties*, rather than dyslexia. A child has a specific learning difficulty when his or her performance on a certain learning task (reading, spelling, numerical skills) falls 28 months behind that

which would be usual for that child's age and overall ability. It can lead to many difficulties in the classroom setting. These children often have good verbal abilities. It can be confusing and upsetting for them not to be able to translate this ability into their reading, writing or spelling skills. It can also be confusing for class teachers who may see a child as underachieving or unmotivated, rather than having a specific problem.

It is not difficult to see that children will often feel bad about their difficulty and may seek to avoid it by distracting behaviour away from the educational activity. They may develop a low self-esteem and become anxious about school. They may be seen as misbehaving or disruptive in class when they avoid the work which is difficult. If the problem is not recognised, the child can move onto becoming a child with behavioural difficulties.

Research now shows us that children with specific learning difficulties are more likely to develop later conduct disorders than children without those problems. It is, however, not an inevitable progression, since it is more the maladaptive responses of the child and others to the learning difficulties which lead to a poor outcome rather than the learning difficulties per se.

Specific learning difficulties may be associated with other problems too. Poor co-ordination, and difficulties with concentration and overactivity are more often seen in children with these difficulties than on average.

Management issues in Specific Learning Difficulties
The Child Mental-Health Services can be useful in:

- Addressing secondary behaviour difficulties
- Assessing overactivity and poor concentration
- Detecting or diagnosing Specific Learning Difficulties in the above as a presenting problem
- Advising other professionals and agencies

Psychological testing is necessary always to diagnose Specific Learning Difficulties, and ordinarily an educational psychologist would do this. Sometimes, however, the clinical psychologist with Child and Adolescent Mental Health services can also contribute to assessment.

Once the diagnosis has been made, the most important next step is that parents and professionals alike are aware of the specific areas of difficulty which the child has. The Education Department will then make Special Needs provision for the extra teaching input necessary, and it is helpful for parents to have regular communication set up with their child's teachers. Sometimes extra tuition from specialist teachers outside of school may be helpful, as long as there is good communication between school and tutor.

Acknowledgement of the problem and appropriate educational measures can go a long way towards improving concerns over a child's difficult behaviour or low self-esteem. Sometimes the child and their family can need ongoing support and help with these issues, and this is where Child and Adolescent Mental Health services can continue to help after the diagnosis has been made.

Dr Richard Eyres

Summing up...

Unless you have seen an educational psychologist or psychiatrist before, you may feel intimidated by this group of professionals - don't be! Their reports are the main crux of any Statement of Educational Needs. Without them it will be very difficult to ensure the correct provision is identified and carried out.

'Don't mind us, Mrs Jones...just pretend that we're not here... now, tell us about your son...'

5 SCHOOLS

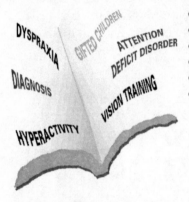

DYSPRAXIA
GIFTED CHILDREN
ATTENTION DEFICIT DISORDER
DIAGNOSIS
VISION TRAINING
HYPERACTIVITY

- State schools
- Independent schools
- Specialist schools
- Do it yourself
- Private tutors
- Summing up...

It is very difficult for anyone to advise on the type of school you should be looking for as every child's needs are so different. For the majority of children they will simply go to the school in their immediate vicinity. But specialist schooling is slightly different, because there is not usually a lot of choice. It is best to speak to as many people as you can including teachers, the education authority's advisors and other parents - the decision is then up to you.

There are many different types of schools including:

- Mainstream schools (your local school)
- Schools for behavioural problems
- Schools for deaf children
- Schools for blind children
- Schools for disabled children

- Schools for children with a mental handicap
- The Independent Sector
- Specialist: art, drama, sports schools with a great emphasis on art etc

State schools

Most of these are ordinary mainstream schools. But there are an increasing number of *specialist* schools for people with *disabilities* and others for pupils with *behavioural* problems.

A booklet is available from all Local Education Authorities with the details of all mainstream and specialist schools. Contact your LEA for further details.

Independent schools

Isis - The independent school's information service has details of schools in the independent sector.

Specialist schools

This covers a very wide area from specialist behaviour

schools, through to dyslexic, blind, deaf, handicapped schools and many others.

Many charities, including the Royal National Institute for the Blind and the Royal National Institute for the Deaf, have several specialist schools. They also give help, guidance and training to mainstream schools, in order that the majority of children can stay in their local schools.

There are specialist schools for Specific Learning Difficulties/dyslexia. These are approved by the Independent Schools Joint Council and the Council for the Registration of Schools.

Do it yourself

Parents who are frustrated by low educational standards can now set up their own school. The government says providing people satisfy the criteria they can *opt in* to the state system and receive government funding.

The Secretary of State decides if there is a need for a school in the area.

If you were considering the above, the school would be *grant maintained* and follow the national curriculum.

Further information is available from, Grant Maintained Schools, 36 Greatsmith Street, London, SW1P 3BU

Private tutors

If your child is struggling at school sometimes a tutor providing one-to-one or two-to-one tuition will make a great deal of difference. Expect to pay approximately £15.00 per hour, and more for subjects with a scarcity value. Lessons take place normally after school. Word of mouth is the best recommendation. The Association of Tutors will tell you about tutors in your area.

Further information is available from: British Dyslexia Association or the Association of Tutors (details in the Help List at the back of this book).

Summing up...

It is important that the correct school is identified for your child. Sometimes, although a school is on your doorstep, it may not always be the best one for *your* child's specialist needs. Visit all the schools in your area and see what specialist provision they can offer.

Some parents also supplement mainstream education with private tutors, which can help tremendously.

6 MEDICAL PROBLEMS

- Arranging a medical
- Deafness
- Blindness
- Vitamins and health
- Summing up...

There are many medical reasons possible for a student's failing at school. Most obviously, if he cannot see or hear properly he will not be able to read/write or respond appropriately. If you suspect your child may have a problem, this should be checked immediately. Your doctor or health visitor will be able to arrange for a medical or hearing test. Your local opticians will carry out a full eye test, even with very young children.

Problems affecting your child at school could result from:

- Blindness
- Deafness
- Temporary deafness
- Lack of vitamins and nourishment
- Physical disability

- Mental disability

Arranging a medical

If the school is concerned that your child is not performing as well as he should be at school, and they have asked for an *Assessment of Educational Needs*, part of the assessment will include a medical. The medical will be carried out in your own home, and you can express any concerns you have with the doctor.

Deafness

Over eight million people suffer from a hearing loss in this country. Over 65,000 of these are children. Deafness is often associated with older people. But many are born deaf or profoundly deaf - others become so after an illness. One million children (0-8 years) will experience *temporary deafness* caused by *glue ear*.

Pardon! What did you say?
If your child cannot hear properly this may be causing his problems and there may be a simple remedy which can correct the problem almost immediately. Wax in the ear canal is the most common problem. Wax is made normally but becomes a problem if excessive amounts are

produced. It then forms into small beads, mixes with dust and dead skin and falls out of the ear. This cleaning mechanism works well for most people and does not need help with cotton tipped sticks or fingers etc. Pushing things into the ear causes more wax and can push the wax firmly down into the drum resulting in pain and deafness. Some people make abnormal amounts of wax and may have to have it removed by a doctor or nurse.

Glue Ear

This is a common condition in childhood. The tube becomes obstructed by adenoids at the back of the nose. The air cannot enter the middle ear, and the cavity fills with fluid. The ear drum becomes dark looking. As time goes on the fluid becomes thicker until it has the consistency of thick glue. Often the only sign is deafness and children's schooling may suffer and behaviour may deteriorate.

In a lot of cases it will clear by itself but in severe cases treatment will involve making a small hole in the drum, usually under a general anaesthetic. A tube (grommet) may be inserted; then the adenoids may be removed. Adenoids usually disappear at puberty and most children with *glue ear* do not need treatment after this time. The hearing is usually restored to normal.

Do deaf children have to attend a special school?

A large percentage of children attend ordinary mainstream schools. Many of them receive additional special education support within their schools.

Blindness

Sight loss is one of the commonest causes of disability in the UK. Almost a million people are blind or partially sighted - one in sixty. Your local opticians can test your child. This test is available under the National Health and is free for children. The test will rapidly reveal whether or not there are difficulties with vision, which could be causing problems in reading and writing. Sometimes a simple pair of glasses can solve the problems. Breathe a sigh of relief!

However, if there is a problem which they feel needs further investigation, they can refer the child to the Orthoptic Department at your local hospital.

Royal National Institute for the Blind

This charity offers help and services to the blind or partially-sighted. They aim to give children with sight impairment the best possible start in life. With the right help these children can perform as well as any other youngsters.

What is the Chronically Sick and Disabled Persons Act?

If you have a child who has a hearing or sight loss they have rights under the *Chronically Sick and Disabled Persons Act (1970)*. What a mouthful! Simply put, it means that local authorities have a duty to provide services to people with disabilities.

There are lots of services which your child may be entitled to. Before you can receive help, he will need to have his needs correctly assessed. Contact your local social services department for further information. Assessments will be arranged by the relevant social worker or doctor. If your child is assessed as requiring a service, the authority has a duty to provide it (although they may charge for this service).

If the local authority refuses to provide a service, you have every right to complain. In the first instance you should complain to the council itself (they all have complaints procedures in place, ask for a copy). If you do not have any success, contact the Citizens Advice Bureau or Local Government Ombudsman for assistance.

Where can I get help?

The *Royal National Institutes for the Deaf, the National Deaf Children's Society, and the Royal National Institute of the Blind* all actively work to promote the views of deaf/

partial deaf and blind people. They campaign in particular for integrated schooling and encourage greater public awareness to these problems.

Vitamins and health

The debate on vitamins and health continues to rage and does not appear to be abating. Recent research shows that children who have a decent breakfast before exams perform much better than those who skip breakfast or just have a bowl of cornflakes. According to a study in the United States the likely explanation is that sugar in the breakfast provides a short-lived surge in blood glucose levels. Thereby brain functioning improves within a short period of time.

In a separate study published in November 1996, another American group of scientists said teenage girls also improved if they were given iron supplements. Previous research appears to show that anaemia affects the mental abilities of children. Animal research has also hinted that iron deficiency is enough to change brain iron levels - which in turn alters the way neurotransmitters behave in the brain.

So many people work and spend time rushing from here to there, grabbing frozen meals. Are our children missing out on vital vitamins they need, not only to grow but also to develop their mental capacities? Research seems to support the theory that some children are not receiving *adequate* vitamins.

Proof of the primrose

Two British women have won a 15-year battle to prove they know more than medical experts about the causes of hyperactivity in children. Vicky Colquhoun and her daughter Sally Bunday, who founded the Chichester-based Hyperactive Children's Support Group, first put a radical proposal forward in 1980.

The women, who have no scientific or medical qualifications, noted that children with hyperactivity or ADD, often had other symptoms such as excessive thirst, dry skin and allergies. They carried out a survey of over 200 hyperactive children and concluded their condition was linked to biochemical problems. These problems were caused by deficiency of essential fatty acids. Two of these fatty acids are supplied by evening primrose oil. When children in the survey took this oil, their behaviour became less hyperactive. Unfortunately, the scientific establishment never took this evidence seriously.

An American journal of clinical nutrition has now confirmed Mrs Colquhoun and Mrs Bunday's findings after almost 15 years. Other research recently confirms that dyslexic children with vision abnormalities can be remedied by essential fatty acids. A supplement called Efalex has been launched which contains these missing fatty acids. These tablets are now available in some larger chemist shops. Further information is available from: Dr B J Story, Senior Lecturer in Nutrition, School of Biological Sciences, University of Surrey.

Summing up...

If your child is suffering from a medical problem, it stands to reason that he may not be able to hear/see what is being said, especially if he sits at the back of the classroom. Ensure that all medical checks have been carried out to ensure peace of mind.

Whilst the debate regarding vitamin supplements continues, the experts seem to disagree with each other constantly. Some argue that our children receive a *good balanced diet* and they do not need to take vitamin supplements to improve their education. Others say that with vitamin supplements children will make faster progress.

There have only been a limited number of trials over the last few years. However, these indicate that people with learning difficulties may improve substantially if vitamin supplements are used.

Without any concrete evidence, and any guidance from the government, the decision has to be left to you.

7 VISION TRAINING

- The role of the orthoptist
- The Dunlop test
- Optometric evaluation
- How do we find you?
- Summing up...

The Role of the Orthoptist

By Christine Robinson DBO, SRO

Children with Specific Learning Difficulties may sometimes need to be referred to the orthoptist for a *Dunlop test*. The tests carried out by the orthoptist help to analyse whether there are any contributory visual problems associated with the learning difficulties. Orthoptists are well qualified to test your child when there are specific learning difficulties. They are specially trained therapists who, among other things, assess vision for close work and distance, and binocular function (how well the two eyes work together).

Some orthoptists have a special interest in assessing children with Specific Learning Difficulties. They do not promise a miraculous cure if treatment is undertaken, but may improve the visual information processing, which can cause great problems for these children. Most of the children will still need specialised teaching.

How do I arrange referral to an orthoptist?

NHS referrals require a letter of introduction from your GP or the school doctor. Some orthoptists are happy to see private patients, and in this instance a referral letter from your GP is not always essential. It is advisable to check the availability of these tests in your area, as not all orthoptic departments are able to undertake this work.

What will the testing involve?

The Dunlop test is one small part of your child's orthoptic assessment. The orthoptist will usually take a full case history, including details of any past treatment for eye problems.

The tests will include:

- Tests to eliminate the presence of a squint ie 'cross eyed'
- Checking of eye movements and ability to scan and pursue a moving target
- Ability of the two eyes to look in together at a near point - ie convergence
- The ability of both eyes to focus clearly on print at a near point - ie accommodation
- Stereoscopic vision - ie 3D vision

- Reserves of muscle ability present to maintain comfortable use of both eyes together

- The Dunlop test - to determine whether there is a reference eye well established

The Dunlop test

The test originated in Australia in 1971 and was designed by Mrs P Dunlop, an orthoptist. Much research has been done in this country by Dr J Stein, physiologist, and Mrs S Fowler, orthoptist (Royal Berkshire Hospital, Reading).

The test involves looking into a special machine at pictures that help us to decide which eye is in charge of sending a message, in the form of a picture, to the language centre in the brain, to decipher what the picture (ie word) says.

It is a two-eyed test - both eyes are open, and we learn whether a reference, or *lead eye*, is established.

This should not be confused with a *dominant eye* which is tested when you hold a tube or kaleidoscope to one eye - invariably the other eye is automatically closed.

Will treatment be needed?
Once the tests are completed, your orthoptist will be able to discuss the findings with you.

If the vision is reduced, you will need to see an optician or ophthalmologist (specialist eye doctor) to check that the eyes are healthy, and to have glasses ordered if necessary.

If there is no reference eye and the child is over seven years old, special glasses with one lens frosted over may be prescribed for all reading, writing and number work. This is not a self help treatment, and progress will need to be monitored carefully by your orthoptist. If your child already has a fixed reference eye, then it is unlikely that frosted glasses will be needed.

Sometimes children with dyslexia need eye exercises to improve the accurate use of both eyes together at a near point. Indeed, they often admit that the words and letters move about or go fuzzy - they may not have commented on this as they think everyone else sees things in the same way!

Aims of treatment
- To develop a reference eye.
- To have a good ability to look in to a near point with both eyes together, and maintain a clear picture (convergence and accommodation).
- To have good smooth eye movements in scan and pursuit
- To have good muscle reserves (fusional ability).

How long will treatment last?
If treatment is recommended, it could be as little as one month for exercises, or up to a maximum of one year if frosted glasses are prescribed.

If a reference eye does not become established after a maximum of one year, treatment will be stopped.

If treatment is suggested it is certainly worth a try as there is nothing to lose and it may prove to be extremely beneficial.

By Christine Robinson

Optometric evaluation
by Keith Holland, B.Sc, FBCO, DCLP

In order to be able to concentrate, absorb information and maintain interest in the written word the visual system of a young person has developed certain capabilities. The eyes have to be capable of moving smoothly and easily along a line of print, jumping back and down to the beginning of the next line and repeating this action for extended periods of time.

Students also have to be able to adjust the focus of their eyes rapidly from distance to near and back again when copying from a blackboard.

Conscious or subconscious?
It is important that these activities can be performed without conscious thought or effort. If the brain has to 'use up' concentration and energy in order to simply move the eyes along a line of print, then there is less likelihood that the contents of the text will have any meaning, that it will be remembered, or that the words which are coming next

will be anticipated. Reading has to become a subconscious action.

Learning to read

Learning to move the eyes in a way which enable us to read efficiently is, like changing gear, a learned action. Some young people fail to develop this skill and as a result their reading and writing ability are often lower than expected.

Other skills such as ball-catching or graceful gymnastic body movements can also be affected and children with poorly developed vision systems are frequently observed to be clumsy and ill-coordinated.

Behavioural Optometry

Some fully qualified and state registered optometrists, now additionally practice what is called Behavioural Optometry. Behavioural optometrists operate on the basis that visual skills are learned and therefore trainable.

Vision is considered to be an inseparable part of the whole human system and should not be regarded as a separate and individual function. This means that our behaviour and our environment can influence the way in which our visual system works, and vice versa.

Behavioural optometrists use activities and training to improve the efficiency of the whole visual system.

Vision training

Vision training or vision therapy, provides a means of learning to use the visual system in a more efficient manner. When the visual system works more efficiently, more information can be received, processed and understood. When there are problems with visual perception, understanding vision input, achieving full potential, can be helped by using the techniques of vision training.

This involves developing good body bilaterality, hand-eye coordination, form perception, directional and visualisation skills as well as ensuring that the muscles which focus and direct the eyes are functioning efficiently. Should vision training be necessary these terms will become more meaningful as the therapy programme progresses.

Who can benefit?

Students with good visual abilities read faster with less effort, understand more of what they read and retain it longer. Athletes who use their vision effectively see things more quickly, more accurately and show good overall performance.

The improvement in the processing of visual information can benefit many areas of life, especially at school, in sports and at work.

Optometric vision training is individually programmed to the specific needs of each patient, with the basis universally needed skills being included in all programmes. Other activities are designed to meet specific needs.

What to look for

Children who may benefit from vision training can often be seen when reading to have difficulty in keeping their place and in following lines of print.

Typically a child will read with a finger or a marker under the line being read. As they read they will move the whole of the head rather than simply following the print with their eyes. In many cases mathematical ability and intelligence may be normal or higher than normal for the age, and yet reading presents a problem.

The concentration span of a young person with a poorly developed visual system will be often very short, and time spent reading coming to an abrupt halt with sudden complete lack of interest.

Who can help?

Obviously if a child has learning difficulties all avenues of possible help have to be explored. In order to establish if there may be a visual component to the learning difficulty, a full eye examination must be carried out by an optometrist.

If it is suspected that there may be a developmental visual problem - in other words that all the bits are there and healthy, but not co-ordinating properly - then your optometrist may wish to deal with this himself. Alternatively you may choose to be referred to a behavioural optometrist who has more experience in helping with learning problems.

by Keith Holland

How do we find you?

The British Association of Behavioural Optometrists maintain a register of all Optometrists who have attended a further education course specifically designed to develop their knowledge and skills. A list is available from them (address in the Help List at the back).

Summing up...

The Dunlop test and vision training have often seemed to be surrounded in mystery. It quite simply means, fully testing the eyes and *training* them to respond to appropriate treatment. The treatment may take a few months or several years. If successful it can be a tremendous help to the child. These tests are usually carried out in Optometrist Departments in Hospitals rather than at your local optician's.

8 EDUCATION OUTSIDE SCHOOL

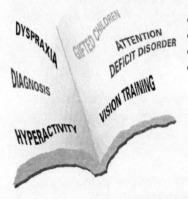

- Education of sick children
- Exclusions from school
- Education otherwise
- Summing up...

Education of sick children

All children fall ill from time to time. If your child is off sick for under four weeks, the school will provide work to be done at home (where the child's condition allows) in order that the child does not miss out on the syllabus etc. It is the LEA's responsibility to make arrangements for the education of sick children.

However, if your child is to stay at home for more than four weeks, he should receive home tuition. The LEAs should take into account how the absence will affect the child when he returns to school.

Education in Hospital
The 1993 Education Act states that children of school age
because of illness or injury must receive *suitable*
education, either at home, or in hospital teaching units.
These teaching units must reflect the National Curriculum,
although this is not mandatory in hospital schools. If a
pupil is admitted to a hospital for more than six days then
it is expected that properly planned provisions are
available to help reintegration to mainstream schools once
the child is better.

It is vital that liaison between the school and hospital is
ongoing in order to provide an effective educational
programme.

Where can I get further information?
Further information can be obtained from: Department for
Education and Employment, Sanctuary Buildings, Great
Smith Street, London, SW1P 3BT. Tel 0171 925 5533.
Education of Sick Children, Circular number 12/94, DH
LAC (94) 10, NHSE HSG (94) 24.

Exclusions from school

Last year approximately 11,000 children were excluded
from school and the number is growing each year.
Exclusion from school can be a distressing and isolating
experience for young people and their parents.

Temporary exclusions - who can exclude my child?
The Headmaster (or *very rarely* the Deputy Head) is the
only person who may exclude a child from school for up to
15 school days in any *one* term. Exclusions should only be
in response to serious breaches of school's policy on
behaviour or of the criminal law.

School Governors, the LEA and the Independent Appeal
Committee are the different groups of people who can give
permission for your child to go back to school.

Formal notification
Head teachers must on the day of the exclusions contact
the parents and inform them of the reason for exclusion,
the length of the exclusion and the specific reason for it.

The notification:

• must be sent immediately

• should provide enough information about the reason for
  exclusion

• must state, that parents have the right to make representations
  to the governing body and the LEA

• should give them the name and address of the appropriate
  people to contact.

Access to records
The parents have the right to a copy of their child's
records within 15 days of asking for them.

How can I object?

If you wish to object to the exclusion, you should write immediately to the School Governors, the LEA and the Independent Appeal Committee stating your objections. The letters could look like this:

```
To the Chair of Governors

Date



Dear  Sir/Madam

My son (name) has been excluded from
school. I do not think there was just
cause for the exclusion and I would like
to meet the governors so you can consider
his case.

I would like a copy of his school records
immediately. As you are aware, time is of
the essence. I will call at the school to
collect them on (give day).

Yours  faithfully,
```

Sample letter to the governors

```
Date



Dear  Sir/Madam

My son has been excluded from school. I do
not agree with this and I would like to
meet you to discuss the matter further.

Yours  faithfully,


```

Sample letter to the Local Education Authority

Permanent Exclusions

Permanent exclusions must be considered very carefully indeed and are *not* appropriate for minor offences such as:

- Truancy
- Pregnancy
- Drugs
- Breaking the law is not an automatic reason for exclusion

Permanent exclusion should only be sought after all other services have been consulted ie Special Educational Needs Departments, Health, Social Services and LEA's.

Formal Notification

If an exclusion is to be permanent then head teachers:

- must inform the parents as soon as possible

- must state the reasons for permanent exclusion

- must give notice of any relevant previous warnings, fixed period exclusions or other disciplinary measure taken

Can I appeal?

Parents should then appeal using the procedure as for *Temporary Exclusions*.

Where can I get further help and advice contact?

Department for Education and Employment Publications Department. (Circular number 10/94, Exclusions from School.), and Ace Publications (Exclusion from School).

Education otherwise

by Sylvia Jeffs

The Home Education Option

Most children go to school...but they do not have to do so. It is *education which is compulsory*. The law says that is a parent's duty to cause their child to receive efficient full-time education suitable to his age, ability and aptitude and to any Special Educational Needs he may have, either by regular attendance at school, or *otherwise*.

People decide to educate their children at home for a variety of reasons; some may arise from their own convictions or philosophies, others may be due to difficulties encountered within the school system. For example:

- to provide a specific religious environment
- to provide an education different in form or content from that offered
- having enjoyed helping their child with *early years* learning, they see no reason to delegate their responsibility when their child reaches five years old
- schools have failed their child in some way
- their child may be refusing to attend
- bullying
- exclusion

As parents are the people responsible for ensuring their child's education, they do not need permission to provide that education outside the school system. Nor do they have to justify their decision to do so. They are not even legally obliged to inform the LEA if the child is not a registered pupil at a school (eg a child under the age of five; one whose family has moved into a different area too far for him to attend the same school; one who has completed primary education and would otherwise transfer to a secondary school; one who has been permanently excluded).

However, if a home-education family came to their notice, the LEA has a duty to see that the parents are not failing to carry out their responsibility to educate their child. The

LEA is entitled to ask informally for information but has no right to impose specific criteria concerning educational styles or methods.

There are no legal requirements for parents to have teaching qualifications, or to follow the National Curriculum or any other specific syllabus or timetable.

A child who is a registered pupil at a school must be de-registered in accordance with the Pupil's Registration Regulations. For children at mainstream schools this is an automatic procedure, after the head teacher receives written notification from the parent. The regulations do not provide for automatic deregulation from a special school. However, this is not in order to prevent the choice for home education. Since the law requires authorities to act *reasonably*, any LEA who misused the Regulations to try to obstruct or prevent a parent from choosing the home education option would certainly be acting unreasonably.

Although there have been some problems in the past, in recent years the majority of LEAs have accepted that they must not interfere with parents' legal right to choose home-based education for their children. Most are cooperative, many may offer valuable advice and support, and some offer access to resources.

Obviously, individual LEA officers may hold widely differing views on the merits of home education. Many are extremely supportive and enthusiastic, but there are those who are prejudiced or hostile. If this causes difficulties or hinders the development of good relationships, parents can request that another officer be assigned to the case.

Among LEA personnel, parents and various Independent advisory organisations, there are some common areas of misunderstanding about home education for children with special needs; the major misconception being that *Statemented* children may not be *home educated*. This is not true.

This is often unfamiliar territory for LEA officers, and presumably because of the duties imposed on them by the special needs legislation, they may go on to assume the right to decide all aspects of a child's education. Even to the point of denying that the parent has the same right to choose home education as one whose child does not have a Statement.

Statements are intended, not to confer extra rights and powers on LEAs, but to oblige them to arrange for the provision specified to be made *unless the parent has made suitable arrangements*.

It has also been known for LEAs to misinterpret or misunderstand that section of the Education Act which refers to: *education otherwise than at school*. They do not realise that this relates entirely to out-of-school arrangements made by the LEA themselves, and thus has no relevance to provision made by the parents. However, some parents have used this section of the legislation to obtain specific extra provision (usually financial and often related to specialist therapies not available in their county).

Another misconception is that *Statemented* children must be taught by someone who has *special needs training*. This has sometimes given rise to strange demands that parents wishing to home educate must either have relevant special need's qualification themselves, or employ someone who has them. Not true, of course - even in schools many teachers, ancillaries or assistants have no such qualifications.

The growing minority of parents who choose to take direct responsibility for their own child's education outside the school system do not take this decision lightly or on impulse. Education out of school is a major commitment, especially if their child has special needs.

The concern and care of parents can provide a basis for a more effective education in many important ways. In particular:

- the provision of one-to-one teaching or interaction
- the inherent flexibility of the home situation - free from those physical and administrative constrains of the school environment which prevent the possibility of following the interests and motivations of the individual child

Parents are in a better position to understand and cater for all aspects of their child's development and welfare. For example, many children have special dietary needs; schools are often unable or unwilling to make special arrangements or are found to be particularly bad at following those they do make. If the nature of the child's disability means they put on weight easily, suffer from digestive abnormalities which call for more frequent meals, or have food intolerances or allergies, the home is the best place to cater for such problems.

Each family situation is unique, but in general, parents feel that their children learn more positive values at home than those often found in schools. They have a better quality social life because home-educators are not obliged to impose artificial barriers (mainly of age and/or ability) to social contact. The children can mix freely and confidently with people of varying age, ability and background. This helps them to be more socially adaptable, outgoing and mature than many of their school-going counterparts.

This is particularly true for children with Special Educational Needs, who are able to learn from real life - not segregated into special schools; not marked out as different by the presence of extra helpers in mainstream - but truly integrated.

Information, support and practical and legal advice can be obtained from *Education Otherwise* a nationwide self-help membership organisation whose officers and advisers are unpaid volunteers. Membership also offers opportunities for cooperation with like-minded families in a variety of regional and national activities.

By Sylvia Jeffs

Summing up...

We normally think that education is carried out only in schools. But for a variety of reasons there are a percentage of children who are educated outside these establishments. This could be in hospitals, specialist establishments, at home if the child has been expelled, or at home through the parent's choice.

It is the *education* that is compulsory, *not* school.

9 CAN COMPUTERS HELP?

- Hardware
- Software
- Further questions
- Computers in exams
- Summing up...

The last few years have seen great strides in the Information Technology field. There is now a vast array of specialist software for people with learning difficulties. The advances will continue for many years. This chapter does not intend to review the hardware and software on offer but simply provide an 'overview' of the types that are available.

If you are buying a computer for educational purposes, then my advice is to purchase a multimedia computer in order to gain the best out of your educational software.

Hardware

There are three main types of computer available: Acorn, Apple Macintosh and the IBM Compatible.

The latter are now the most popular computers sold throughout the world. As schools replace or add Information Technology suites this is the type they are replacing them with. Most of the computers in this range incorporate speakers and sound cards (ie multimedia) which make it ideal for specialist educational software.

Computers can cost anything from £1,000 upwards. Before purchasing you should ask yourselves:

- What am I most likely to use it for?
- What choices are available? - (limit this to three)
- How much memory do I need?
- Do I need multimedia?
- What are the price differences?
- What other options are there?
- What software is included in the price?
- What guarantee is available?
- What back-up can I expect?

Whichever computer students use, they will gain skills that can be transferred later to any other machine. My personal view is that I would rather students used computers that they are likely to encounter in the business world. This way they are getting first hand knowledge of the computers they will be using when they go to work.

Software

I would recommend three different types of software packages that are a minimum for people with learning difficulties:

Wordprocessor

A Wordprocessor is the most important piece of software required and can be used as a substitute for pen and paper. People with learning difficulties are finding that when they use a word processor, *the written world opens up to them* - at last they can put their thoughts down on paper. Many schools allow children to use computers to complete GCSE course work and they may be allowed to use them for their exams (subject to certain criteria). Students have argued for years that an exam is to test their knowledge not their writing ability!

Most good wordprocessors incorporate a *spellchecker* and a *gramchecker*. Although students may find it difficult to use, a *gramchecker* (as the name implies - checks grammar) is well worth taking the time and effort in learning.

I prefer to use *Microsoft Word* software; this is very simple to use and has a good spellchecker and gramchecker included. Many offices use this software.

Spreadsheets

Excel or Lotus are excellent spreadsheets and can show students who are shy of figures that there is nothing to worry about. The graphs on both of these are easy to use and can help to enhance the student's work in many different ways.

Database

Access is a good package. Databases are difficult to use in the first instance but once mastered they are excellent for organising lists of friends, business acquaintances, homework and assignments.

How can computers help in the classroom setting?

Computers are now an important part of classroom teaching. Although no computer package can ever be a substitute for good teaching, the correct software packages can help and support the busy teacher. Many programmes can be incorporated into a specialist teaching scheme. They provide the essential over-learning, structured and systematic teaching, immediate reinforcement and feedback and the additional motivation that students require to succeed.

The advantage of instant feedback, the possibility of echoing each letter name, each word, each sentence of any marked section of text, as well as reading through, helps the student with the poor short term memory. It ensures an efficient transfer to long term memory - making learning fun. Software packages can provide structured learning, continually developing skills and providing support for literacy and numeracy.

How can computers help learners?

Computers can help people with learning difficulties in lots of different ways:

- Learning to use databases and spreadsheets may aid sequential thinking and problem solving skills.

- Can motivate people, especially children

- There is immediate reinforcement

- Students have the ability to make and self-correct mistakes in private

- Essential over-learning/reinforcement

- Many computers can now be programmed to 'speak to you'. This software could revolutionise foreign language learning. Programmes with speech, make learning truly multi-sensory

- Can listen - ideas developed orally can be tried out and changed easily

- Response is immediate

- Students work at own pace

- Printouts and text on a screen are often easier to read than their own writing

- Reading and spelling is incorporated in nearly every program

Games

Arcade type games, often seen as students just *playing*, can help develop hand/*eye* co-ordination and a fun approach adopted to make learning almost painless.

Sinking battleships in alphabetical order is far more exciting than looking for X,Y,Z etc on a keyboard.

Specialist educational software

Hull University have a specialist department which is affiliated to the British Dyslexia Association. They have many different types of software available. This software is *not only* suitable for people suffering with dyslexia. Students who suffer with other learning difficulties, including physical, may benefit from the phonic structured software.

For further advice on the different types of software, it is best to contact the university direct. If you enclose a stamped addressed envelope, they will be happy to send you information. Please note, they cannot answer telephone calls.

The British Dyslexia Association Computer Committee has been reviewing programs for dyslexia/Specific Learning Difficulties for over 10 years. There is a series of booklets which are updated frequently. Contact Dyslexia Computer Resource Centre.

Speech Training

Computers are now helping children at some schools to learn to speak properly. A *speech training aid* computer displays the word it wants a child to say - and listens to the way the child repeats the word. It then tells them if they have said it correctly. Once the child has said the word correctly, he can move on to the next word. There are over 1,000 words with graphics available. Teachers using the software are impressed at the computer's ability to 'hear' them talking. The project is being developed jointly by the Defence Research Agency and Hereford and Worcester County Council.

If this scheme continues to prove successful, this could be a great help for speech training in the future.

Voice activated computers

Similar to the above. These have been available for a long time, but the latest ones have improved sound systems. Extremely useful for disabled people and anyone learning languages etc.

Touch-screen computers

These computers work by simply *touching the screen* with your hands. They are useful for people with physical difficulties. They are also becoming extremely useful in identifying and assessing very young children (three years) for early signs of Specific Learning Difficulties.

The Hands-free computer
Computers due to go on sale within the next year will have neither screen, keyboard nor mouse. They will be controlled by hand movements in mid-air. The 'virtual computer' will be introduced in offices and operating theatres. Hand movements in mid-air will be picked up by cameras coupled to pattern recognition software and used to control the computer in the same way that is done now, by a mouse. Although these systems will cost over a thousand pounds more than conventional computers, their use will be tremendous for people with all sorts of disabilities.

Further questions

My son has a 'Statement'. Can he get a laptop from school?
Some Local Education Authorities supply laptop computers for children who come under this category. Check with the authority which covers your area.

My son is dyspraxic, and wants to learn to type. Can you suggest some software for him?
Mavis Beacon for Kids is a good touch typing course for children. Price around £30.

Where can I get educational software?
There are thousands of educational programs and many

publishers. Catalogues are available and a few will send programs on approval.

Agents for Software
- **AVP**
  School Hill Centre, Chepstow, Gwent, NP6 5PH.
  Tel 01291 625 439
- **Dyslexia Computer Resource Centre**
  Department of Psychology, University of Hull, Hull, HU6 7RX.
  Tel 01482 465 589
  (No telephone calls, stamped addressed envelopes only.)
- **Dyslexia Educational Resources**
  Broadway Studios, 28 Tooting High Street, London SW17 ORG.
  Tel 0181 672 4465
- **Rickitt Educational Media**
  Great Western House, Westover, Langport, Somerset, TA10 9YU.
  Tel 01458 253 636

Computers in exams

Special Arrangements
The *Examination Board Regulations for Special Arrangements (September 1995)* say that these are made to enable candidates with a disability (eg Specific Learning Difficulty) to show their attainment when otherwise, they might not be able to do so. (Special Arrangements should not give an advantage over other candidates.)

Can my son use a computer for his exams?
There are two questions that need to be answered first:

- Does he have a 'Statement of Educational Needs' and
- Does he normally use a wordprocessor for school work?

If the answer to both these questions is 'yes', there is a good chance that this provision will be allowed.

How do I get permission for him to use it in exams?
- Speak to the school teachers involved and arrange for him to use a wordprocessor at the soonest possible time
- Examination Boards will want to know if the child usually uses the wordprocessor
- Make sure that if the child has a Statement that, *use of IT in assessment and examinations*, is put on it. Do this *before* Key Stage 3
- Long term use of word processing will be taken into account of an educational psychologists' Report

An excellent booklet *Dyslexia (Specific Learning Difficulties), Exams and Word Processing,* by Ted Pottage, £3.00 is available from the British Dyslexia Association.

Summing up...

Computers are a great help in education. Over the last few years in relative terms they have become cheaper, making them more accessible for the average family.

Specialist educational software has greatly improved over the last couple of years. You can now get software to help you learn a language, play the piano or even learn to cook.

For the disabled user there are computers that can *talk to you* and *respond to your voice*. You can also get computers that need neither *keyboard*, nor *mouse*.

10 CAREER OPTIONS

- Further education/career choices
- Psychometric testing
- Work and discrimination
- Summing up...

Further Education/Career Choices

Thinking about career choices whilst still at school is
extremely daunting for the student. But the decision made
at this stage will affect their whole working life. Of course
our experience at school, college and in the workplace
make us consider our careers regularly throughout our
working lives. These days it is unusual to have a job for
life and we have to continue to change over the years.

Careers Advice
All areas of the country are covered by a Careers Office,
although their name has recently been changed (the name

is different all over the country). However, they are still available nationwide to advise your child on their future educational needs.

During the last couple of years at school, most pupils will be given the opportunity of an in-depth interview with a Careers Adviser. The Careers Office holds vast up-to-date information on hundreds of jobs. The interview will be centred around your child to discuss his strengths, interests, ambitions and explain the education and training options open to him. Once this has been completed, a Career Guidance Plan will then be developed which will summarise the meeting and the steps agreed.

The pupil will then have to make a decision about which way he would like to go:

- Further Academic Studies, eg A level or further GCSE's
- Vocational Course - work related courses GNVQ's
- Specific Training or employment

The Adult Literacy Service
The Adult Literacy Service works with your LEA to provide advice and information to students with learning difficulties. The Further Education Funding Council may be able to give additional funding to students with Special Educational Needs. Colleges try to ensure that there are equal opportunities for all potential students.

Psychometric testing

Psychometric testing can help all students. These tests are sometimes arranged in schools in conjunction with the Careers Adviser. They are comprehensive *paper and pencil* tests which provide an objective assessment of an individual's abilities and personality. Information keyed in by the student is matched with possible career choices held on a computer. As a result, a range of suitable careers the student may not have thought of can be suggested. There are many different types of tests around but they are basically similar.

These tests are also available in certain libraries, colleges, other educational establishments and in some private companies.

Most of these tests are simple *tick the box* style:

Place	Like	Dislike	Hours	Like	Dislike
Indoors			Normal hours		
Outdoors			Shifts/rotas		
In one workplace			Early mornings		
In several places			Evenings		
Abroad			On call		

When the form is completed, the answers are fed into a computer, the computer analyses the information and prints out your *likes/dislikes*, *don't minds* and *strong dislike*.

Once completed, scores are entered by the computer into bands.

Range of Scores

The rating given to each job tells you how well the job matches your likes and dislikes. The higher the rating, the more likely it is to suit you.

Scores

061 - 100   Jobs in this range have more of your likes than your dislikes

041 - 060   These jobs have about the same number of your likes or dislikes

000 - 040   Jobs in this range have more of your dislikes than your likes

Job Selection

The computer then prints out the top 20 jobs which best match the answers you gave and enters the minimum qualifications for each job.

Sample of printout

Agricultural/horticultural mechanic   Rating 76
An agricultural/horticultural mechanic - repairs, tests and services agricultural plant or horticultural machinery on farms or in workshops.

<u>Qualifications for young people</u>
BTEC National award: 4 GCSE (grades a-c) including Maths, English and Science or Technical subjects.

<u>Personal qualities</u>
Good with your hands, practical, conscientious, inventive

<u>Similar jobs</u>
Other mechanical jobs.

Work and discrimination

The Disability & Discrimination Act
This brings in new laws aimed at ending the discrimination which many disabled people face. The Act gives disabled people new rights among other things in schools, colleges and the workplace.

Disabled people with a disability making it difficult to carry out normal day to day activities have new rights under this Act. The disability must be substantial, have a long term effect, and could be physical, sensory or mental.

Schools
Schools will have to explain the arrangements for admission of disabled pupils, how they will help pupils

gain access and how they will ensure they are treated fairly.

Colleges
Colleges and Universities will have to publish disability statements containing information about facilities for disabled people.

Employment
It is against the law for an employer to treat a disabled person less favourably than someone else because of their disability, unless there is a good reason to do so. This applies to all employment matters.

This Act does not apply to employers who employ fewer than 20 people. However, *they will be encouraged* to follow good practice guidelines.

There are certain professions which are exempt from applying the above rules.

Complaints
Disabled people who feel discriminated against by an employer may be able to complain to an Industrial Tribunal. Further information available from The Advisory Conciliation and Arbitration Service (ACAS).

Where can I get further information?
For a leaflet on the Disability Discrimination Act write to:
Disability on the Agenda, Freepost, Bristol, BS38 7DE or
telephone 0345 622 633.

Summing up...

A lot of help and advice is now given to pupils at school.
This starts when the pupils are approximately 13-14 years
of age and continues until they leave school. This ensures
that the pupil has been given the option of different career
choices available to them.

With psychometric testing now widely available at some
schools, colleges, universities and career offices, this can
be used as a great tool for the person with special needs.

11 SETTING UP A SUPPORT GROUP

DYSPRAXIA

GIFTED CHILDREN

ATTENTION DEFICIT DISORDER

DIAGNOSIS

VISION TRAINING

HYPERACTIVITY

We all need support at some time or another. When your child has special needs, it is easy to feel as if you are the only one in the world. There are hundreds of children who have problems with their education. What is needed is to bring parents together, to enable them to talk the problems through - to help and advise each other. Your problem will not be a new one. If you are suffering because of it - you can bet there are others out there in the same position.

Why not set up a Support Group?

Why not form a support group in your area? It isn't as hard as it may seem - if you need it there must be others who will be feeling the same. Don't wait until someone else does it - because they might not!

How do I go about it?

- Ask other parents, and see if they are interested in joining

- Visit your local library, Citizens' Advice Bureau or other voluntary agencies to see if they have any information that may help you

- Ask yourself what exactly is needed in your area

- Do you want to have meetings every week/month?

- Where will your meetings be? (The first meeting will probably be best held in a local hall)

- Contact the national charity to see what help they can offer

- It may be possible to get a guest speaker for your first meeting from a national organisation

- Ask other parents to give you a hand. If you don't ask, you don't get, that is my maxim - you can't do everything yourself! It may seem hard at the start but keep going - it gets easier.

Advertising your group?

No, I don't mean by paying for advertisements with the local press. My company does not have an advertising budget at all. *The local radio and newspapers need local news* - let them know what you are doing.

Press Release

The quickest way to let the press know is by *a Press Release*. Don't panic. This is *very easy*. It is just like writing a letter and then taking out all the chitchat leaving just the bones. Something similar to the one following will be sufficient. Don't forget: if you need help, so do other people in the same situation.

Maria Chivers

1 anyroad

Anytown

Anycounty

0123 445678

PRESS RELEASE
SUPPORT GROUP SPECIAL EDUCATIONAL NEEDS

There will be a meeting in West Drayton School Hall, on Wednesday 17th November at 7.30, to discuss the setting up of a Support Group for Special Educational Needs.

There will be a guest speaker, from the British Dyslexia Association who will talk on *'Special Educational Needs - How you can help'*.

The aim is to form a group for parents and carers, providing support and information about services in our area.

There will be a small entrance fee of £1.00.

For further information, please contact Maria Chivers, Tel 0123 445678.

Sample Press Release

And finally...

The British Dyslexia Association is 25 years old, but there is still a need for more public and professional recognition of the problem. Voluntary groups, awareness weeks, conferences and the like all help to achieve this, and we can all support these.

I hope I have answered many of your questions about dyslexia and other learning difficulties. Unfortunately, there is no magic cure, no secret formula. But there is a lot of help and advice available, and I hope I have shown how you could use this to help your child.

Good luck to you all.

HELP LIST

ACE (Advisory Centre for Education)

1b Aberdeen Studios
22 Highbury Grove
London N5 2EA
Tel **0171 354 8321**
A national education advice centre working towards an education system that supports all children. Provides advice on education to parents and schools and produces a wide range of publications.

AFASIC (Overcoming Speech Impairments)

347 Central Market
Smithfield
London EC1A 9NH
Tel **0171 236 3632**
Fax **0171 236 8115**
Helpline for children and young people with speech and language impairments. Support groups nationwide. Membership available with regular publications.

Association for Brain-Damaged Children

Clifton House
3 St. Pauls Road
Foleshill
Coventry CV6 5DE
Tel **01203 665 450**

Association for Spina Bifida and Hydrocephalus

Asbah House
42 Park Road
Peterborough PE1 2UQ
Tel **01733 555 988**
Fax **01733 555 985**
Organisation provides

support to people with spina bifida and hydrocephalus and their carers. Area specialist advisors available.

Association of Educational Psychologists

3 Sunderland Road
Durham DH1 21H
Tel **0191 384 9512**
Fax **0191 386 5287**
This is the trade union for all qualified educational psychologists who work in England, Wales and Northern Ireland may belong.

Association of Tutors

Sunnycroft
63 King Edward Road
Northampton NN1 5LY
Tel **01604 24171** or
Tel 07000 **AOTTEL**
Send a short letter with your telephone number, and brief details about your enquiry. Enclose a stamped addressed envelope.

ATAXIA

The Stable
Wiggins Yard
Bridge Street
Godalming
Surrey GU7 1HW

Tel **01483 417 111**
Charity that supports people and helps to fund research into causes of Ataxia. Support groups in most areas. Membership available with a regular magazine.

National Autistic Society

276 Willesden Lane
London NW2 5RB
Head Office
Tel **0181 451 1114**
Fax **0181 451 5865**
Helpline Tel **0181 830 0999**
Provides help and advice for parents, carers and people with autism.

Behavioural Optometrists

British Association of Behavioural Optometrists
74a High Street
Billericay
Essex CM12 9BS.
Maintain a register of all Optometrists who have attended a further education course specifically designed to develop their knowledge and skills.

British Epilepsy Association

Anstey House
40 Hanover Square
Leeds LS3 1BE
Tel **01132 439 393**
Fax **01132 242 8804**
Help and advice with understanding Epilepsy. Membership available with magazine *Epilepsy Today* to all members.

British Dyslexia Association

98 London Road
Reading
Berkshire RG1 5AU
Tel **01734 66 8271**
Fax **01734 35 1927**
Aims to advance education and employment opportunities for people with Dyslexia. Over 100 local associations working throughout the country. Advice available to both parents and professional bodies on identification and teaching. Membership available with regular magazines. Wide list of books/brochures available.

Centre for Studies on Inclusive Education

1 Redland Close
Elm Lane
Redland
Bristol BS6 6UE
Tel **01171 923 8450**

Citizens Advice Bureux (CAB)

See local phone book for address.
Ensures that individuals do not suffer through ignorance of their rights and responsibilities or of the services available, or through an inability to express their needs effectively.

Contact-a-Family

170 Tottenham Court Road
London W1P OHA
Tel **0171 383 3555**
Fax **0171 383 0259**
Information and support for parents of children with disabilities. Details available of support groups in your areas. Some information available on benefits and services.

Council for Disabled Children

8 Wakely Street
London EC1V 7QE
Tel **0171 843 6000**

Department for Education and Employment

Sanctuary Buildings
Great Smith Street
London SW1P 3BT
Tel **0171 925 5533**
Fax **0171 925 6986**
Government department set up to assist parents and professionals with all aspects of education and employment.

Department for Education and Employment Publications Centre

PO Box 2193
London E15 2EU
Tel **0181 533 2000**
A wide selection of books and leaflets on special educational needs are available in over 10 different languages. Some information is also available on audio cassette and/or in Braille.

Disability Alliance

Ist. Floor East
Universal House
88 - 94 Wentworth Street
London E1 7SA
Helpline Tel **0171 247 8763**
(Mon. & Wed between 2 - 4)

Disabled Living Foundation

380 - 384 Harrow Road
London W9 2HU
Tel **0171 289 6111**
Fax **0171 266 2922**
Provides practical and up to date advice on living with a disability. Enquiry service by letter (large sae required). The information covers: occupational and physiotherapists, specialist equipment, clothing and footwear. Fact sheets available.

Down's Syndrome Association

155 Mitcham Road
London SW17 9PG
Tel **0181 682 4001**
Offers help and support to families and carers of people with Down's Syndrome and

the professionals who work with them. Information available on all aspects of the condition.

Dyslexia Computer Resource Centre (for BDA Software)

Department of Psychology
University of Hull
Hull HU6 7RX
Tel 01482 465 589
Specialist software for computers. Works closely with the British Dyslexia Association. Various software packages available. Help and advice. Unable to take any phone calls. (Large sae required)

Dysphraxia Foundation

8 West Alley
Hitchin
Hartfordshire SG5 1EG
Tel **01462 454986**
Fax **01462 455052**
Information and advice on Dyspraxia. Over 40 local coordinators around country. Membership available.

Educational Advisory Service

Fiddlers wood

Bredon
Nr Tewkesbury
Gloucester GL20 7QN
Tel **01684 772897**
Advisory service to parents on diagnostic screening for vision-related learning and literacy difficulties.

Education Otherwise

PO Box 7420
London N9 9SG
Tel **0891 518303**
A nationwide self-help organisation. Support, practical and legal advice available. Membership offers opportunities for co-operation with like-minded families in a variety of regional and national activities.

Gifted Children's Information Centre

Hampton Grange
21 Hampton Lane
Solihull B91 2QJ
Tel **0121 705 4547**
Help and advice available to parents and professionals in identifying 'gifted' children. Publishes a series of handbooks.

Local Government Ombudsman

Commission for Local
Administration in England
21 Queen Anne's Gate
London SW1H 9BU
Tel **0171 915 3210**
Fax **0171 233 0396**
Government Ombudsman
set up to look into
complaints from people
about various matters
including Education Appeal
Committees. The
Ombudsmen are
independent of other
organisations.

Hyperactive Children's Support Group

71 Whyke Lane
Chichester
West Sussex PO19 2LD
Tel **01903 725182**
National and local support
groups, providing information
for parents with a
hyperactive child. Helpline
Weekdays 10 - 1pm

I Can

Barbican City Gate
1-3 Dufferin Street

London EC1Y 8NA
Tel **0171 374 4422**
Fax **0171 374 2762**
Charity providing for speech
and language difficulties for
children from nursery to 16
years. Helpline and leaflets
available.

IPSEA (Independent Panel for Special Education Advice)

22 Warren Hill Road
Woodbridge
Suffolk IP12 4DU
Tel **01394 382814**
Helpline Mon - Thurs 10 - 4.
Evenings 7 pm - 9pm.
Gives independent, expert
advice about special
education.

Kids

80 Waynflete Square
London W10 6UD
Tel **0181 969 2817**
Fax **0181 969 4550**
Charity established over 25
years. Aims to provide local
services to families with
children who have special
needs.

MENCAP

123 Golden Lane
London EC1Y ORT
Information Line-
Tel **0171 696 5593** (2pm - 5pm)
Mencap was 50 years old in 1996 and is one of the leading charities, who provide information on a number of services - education, respite care, training workshops to people with a learning disability and their families.

MIND (National Association for Mental Health)

Granta House
15 Broadway
London E15 4BQ
Tel **0181 519 2122**
Fax **0181 522 1725**
Provides care in the community for people with mental health problems. Health and advice for carers of people.

National Deaf Children's Society

15 Dufferin Street
London EC1Y 8PD
Tel Voice & Text-
0171 250 0123
Fax **0171 251 5020**
Freephone **0800 252 380**
(Mon - Fri. 2 - 5)
Organisation to help families, parents and carers which exist to enable deaf children to maximise their skills and abilities, and works to remove all the barriers which hinder this process.

National Federation of the Blind of the UK

Unity House
Smyth Street
Westgate
Wakefield
West Yorkshire WF1 1ER
Tel **01924 291313**
Fax **01924 200 244**
Campaigning organisation to make life easier for blind/partial blind people. Current issues: *Cycle-ways, Streetwise and Integrated Education.*

Network 81

1-7 Woodfield Terrace
Chapel Hill
Stansted
Essex CM24 8AJ
Tel **01279 647 415**
Fax **01279 816 438**

Offers practical help and support to parents throughout all stages of assessment and statementing as outlined in the education act 1993. The helpline offers an individual service linked to a National Network of local contacts. A wide range of literature aimed at familiarising parents with the assessment and statementing procedures is available.

People First

Instrument House
207 Kings Cross Road
London WC1X 9DB
Tel **0171 713 6400**
Fax **0171 833 1880**
Self advocacy groups for people with learning difficulties.

Physiotherapy

The Chartered Society of Physiotherapy
14 Bedford Row
London WC1R 4ED
Tel **0171 242 1941**
Fax **0171 306 6611**

Pre-school Learning Alliance (Playgroup Association)

69 Kings Cross Road
London WC1X 9LL
Tel **0171 833 0991**
Fax **0171 837 4942**
A national educational charity with more than 30 years experience in pre-school and education. It has a membership of over 20,000. Drop in centres in various areas for families needing extra support.

Physically Disabled and Able Bodied (PHAB Ltd)

Summit House
Wandle Road
Croydon CR0 1DF
Tel **0181 667 9443**
Fax **0181 681 1399**
A national body which works for further integration of disabled people. Over 350 clubs. Helpline and leaflets available.

RADAR (Royal Association for Disability and Rehabilitation)

12 City Forum
250 City Road
London, EC1V 8AF
Tel **0171 250 3222**
Fax **0171 250 0212**
(Minicom 0171 250 4119)
National organisation working with physically disabled people. Information and advice available for all aspects of disabilities. Publishes a newsletter each month.

RNIB (Royal National Institute for the Blind)

224 Great Portland Street
London W1N 6AA
Tel **0171 388 1266**
Fax **0171 388 2034**
RNIB is the leading charity working for blind and partially sighted people. Help, information and support is available, in order that blind and partially sighted people can live independently. There are over 60 services available.

RNID (Royal National Institute for Deaf People)

19-23 Featherstone Street
London EC1Y 8SL
Tel **0171 296 9000**
(voice)
Fax **0171 296 8199**
Text **0171 296 800011**
The RNID is the leading charity representing the interests of both deaf and hard of hearing people. It campaigns for improvements in facilities and services and for more awareness of deafness by both government bodies and members of the public.

SCOPE (formerly the Spastics Society)

12 Park Crescent
London W1N 4EQ
Tel **0171 636 5020**
Fax **0171 436 2601**
Helpline **0800 626216**
(1pm - 10pm)
Advice and support for families caring for someone with Cerebral Palsy. Advice on education and benefits.

**SKILL - National Bureau
for Students with
Disabilities**

336 Brixton Road
London SW9 7AA
Membership/Publications etc
Head Office.
Tel **0171 2740565**
Helpline **0171 978 9890**
(1.30 - 4.30).
Organisation to help
students and parents in
Further Education with
Learning Difficulties and
Disabilities.

Help Yourself To A Job
Jackie Lewis ISBN 1-86144-033-2
£7.99 147 pp

Jackie Lewis's practical guide will give you the 'think smart' job-hunting skills you need to compete in today's tough market. She tackles head-on the special problems encountered by career-changers, or those already unemployed. Her simple activities will boost your confidence and get you thinking and moving towards your job goal right away. Jackie has helped hundreds of Job Club clients find the job they wanted using this creative person-centred approach.

Forget The Fear Of Food
Dr Christine Fenn ISBN 1-86144-035-9
£7.99 148 pp

Stop dieting and start living! A leading nutritionist explains why slimming diets don't work, and shows how developing self-esteem is the key to changing our eating habits. Packed with practical tips and activities to help you gain control over your eating and your life.

'A new approach . . . grab this book' *Dr Mary Cursiter*

Subfertility: A Caring Guide For Couples
Dr Phyllis Mortimer ISBN 1-86144-025-1
£7.99 104pp

Dr Mortimer gives a thorough and easy to understand
explanation of the why, when and hows of conception,
arming couples with the information they need to start
looking at possible causes and solutions. She provides
expert advice, encouragement and practical help to
couples experiencing both major and minor fertility
problems.

A Parent's Guide To Drugs
Judy Mackie ISBN 1-86144-028-6
£7.99 103 pp

Judy Mackie's no-nonsense guide addresses the questions
about drugs that concern parents most, and arms them
with the information they need to communicate effectively
with their children. Whether you suspect your child, or
their friends, may be taking drugs, or are simply worried
by the horror stories and headlines - this practical guide
will take you through the facts and basic steps, which you
can use and develop to suit your own circumstances.

Education Matters
David Abbott ISBN 1-86144-029-4
£7.99 123 pp

Help yourself to some parent power and help your child get the most out of education. If you've ever felt confused by the new curriculum, or by school administration, don't be. Teacher David Abbott cuts through the jargon with straight facts and clear advice. Covers all you need to know, from what the Education Act means for your child, to how to check your child's real progress and talk to their teacher. Any parent can use this practical guide to help their child become a winner.

Make The Most Of Your Retirement
Mike Mogano ISBN 1-86144-037-5
£7.99 150 pp Pub Feb 98

Why shouldn't you expect your retirement to be fun? asks Mike Mogano. Your retirement can be an expanding world of opportunity, if you organise your finances first, and look out for problems that can come up. Plus he offers hundreds of ideas for ways to use your new-found freedom. Thoughtful discussion and creative suggestions help you make the most of the life you've been waiting for.

Starting School
Lyn Carter ISBN 1-86144-031-6
£7.99 123 pp

Gives the information and advice you need to help your child to a happy and positive primary school experience. Shows how to plan for a good start, and suggests how to deal with problems that might come up. A good start to primary school lays the foundation for a successful education for your child. This book will help you create an enjoyable experience your child can build on in the future.

The Facts About The Menopause
Elliot Philipp ISBN 1-86144-034-0
£7.99 150 pp Pub Feb 98

Elliot Philipp, a consultant gynaecologist, answers the questions women most often ask about the menopause, its symptoms and treatments. He explains what the menopause is, evaluates HRT and alternative therapies, and offers practical advice on problems which can occur at this time.

This complete guide gives women the facts they need to approach their menopausal years with confidence.

Make The Most Of Being A Carer
Ann Whitfield ISBN 1-86144-036-7
£7.99 150 pp

If you are caring for someone with special needs, such as age, disability or ill-health, this is the guide you can turn to. Ann Whitfield, a social worker for many years, and herself a carer, offers expert, reliable and accessible advice covering the financial, legal, emotional and practical aspects of caring.

The problems of caring can be worrying, but they don't have to overwhelm you. This guide will point you to the help you need, and show you what you can do to better life for yourself and the person you care for.

Single Parent Power
Jackie Lewis ISBN 1-86144-038-3
£7.99 150 pp

A training and careers expert, herself a working single mother, explains how to make the most of government and other help available for lone parents. Shows how to plan for a career with prospects, and increase your earning power before going back to work. Details affordable childcare options, and tells how to build a social support network to help you keep going in emergencies. Whether you want to return to work in 5 weeks, 5 months, or 5 years, this is your guide to taking charge and making it happen the way you want.

Need2Know

Thank you for buying one of our books. We hope you found it an enjoyable read and useful guide. Need2Know produce a wide range of informative guides for people in difficult situations. Available in all good bookshops, or alternatively direct from:

Need2Know
Remus House
Coltsfoot Drive
Woodston
Peterborough
PE2 9JX
Order Hotline: 01733 898103
Fax: 01733 313524

Titles

____	**Buying A House**	£5.99
____	**Stretch Your Money**	£4.99
____	**Breaking Up**	£5.99
____	**Superwoman**	£4.99
____	**Work For Yourself And Win**	£5.99
____	**The Expatriate Experience**	£6.99
____	**You And Your Tenancy**	£5.99
____	**Improving Your Lifestyle**	£5.99
____	**Safe As Houses**	£5.99
____	**The World's Your Oyster**	£5.99
____	**Everything You Need2Know About Sex**	£5.99
____	**Travel Without Tears**	£5.99
____	**Prime Time Mothers**	£5.99
____	**Parenting Teenagers**	£5.99
____	**Planning Your Wedding**	£5.99